YOUR FAVOURITE
BEDTIME STORIES
by Uncle Arthur
5

Illustrations by Annette Agard

ISBN 0-904748-74-X
5-vol. set 0-904748-75-8

Printed and published by
The Stanborough Press Ltd.
Alma Park, Grantham, Lincs., NG31 9SL
England

CONTENTS

They heard the angels sing

Bang! Boom! Bang! Boom! Boom!

The bombs were dropping all around. Buildings were burning and falling. People were screaming and crying.

Already most of the city of Surabaya had been destroyed in the terrible bombardment. Thousands of men, women and children had been killed.

Almost all the churches had been blasted, all except the little Adventist church, where Christian and Ketty, with their father and mother and some friends, were talking together, wondering if it would be their turn to die next.

As the bomb-bursts came nearer and nearer they could see, through the windows, great fires blazing all about them. Father, who was the minister of the church, urged them all to take refuge in the baptismal tank. It was not much of an air raid shelter, but the best they had.

This tank, which was behind the church, was not very large or deep, but they all crowded into it and began to pray.

What a prayer meeting that was!

Father prayed, and Mother, then the children. Christian, just 12 years old, remembered the words in the thirty-fourth psalm which say, 'The angel of the

Lord encamps round about them that fear him, and delivers them.'

Over and over again he pleaded: 'Send the angels, Lord, to encamp round about us and deliver us. Send the angels, Lord! Send the angels!'

Then little Ketty, who was only 4, began to plead: 'Dear Jesus, You have promised to send Your angels. Keep Your promise. Jesus, send the angels!'

So they prayed.

And God in heaven heard.

What happened next may seem to some unbelievable. But it really, happened. I know this minister well. He is one of God's noblest servants, and he told me the story himself.

As they prayed, so the planes passed over and the bombs fell farther and farther away. When the sky seemed clear again Father went back into the church to see if all was well. It was. Not a spark of fire had landed on the building.

As he stood there thanking God for His goodness, there came a loud knocking on the door. Going to see who it could be at such a time, he found two policemen there with many angry people behind them.

'Who was singing in this church just now?' they demanded.

'Singing?' he said. 'Singing? Nobody. The church has been empty.'

'You're not telling the truth,' they said. 'We heard the singing, and we want to know what you mean

by singing in here when the city is burning and people are dying all around you.'

'Come in and see for yourself,' said Father.

They came, and found the place empty, and went away wondering.

So did Father. What could the police mean by saying that there had been singing in the church? He hadn't heard any.

Then the bombers returned. The dreadful roar of their engines became louder and louder again. Once more the bombs began to fall. So Father hurried back to the baptismal tank and told the others the strange story the police had told him.

Then they prayed again. Once more, as the noise and terror of it all mounted all about them, Christian and Ketty lifted up their voices to God saying: 'Send the angels! Send the angels, Jesus. Keep Your promise! Send the angels.'

And then they heard it too, that strange, sweet sound. Above the din of destruction, above the bombing and the burning, they heard the sound of singing. Beautiful singing, such as they had never heard before. And it was coming from the church, just as the police had said.

And the song? It sounded, so he told me, just like the old, familiar hymn:

> 'All the way my Saviour leads me;
> What have I to ask beside?
> Can I doubt His tender mercy,
> Who through life has been my guide?

Heavenly peace, divinest comfort,
Here by faith in Him to dwell!
For I know whate'er befall me,
Jesus doeth all things well.

'All the way my Saviour leads me;
Oh, the fullness of His love!
Perfect rest to me is promised
In my Father's house above;
When I wake to life immortal,
Wing my flight to realms of day
This my song through endless ages –
Jesus led me all the way.'

When the bombers had passed, all of them hurried into the church. But still it was empty, without a sign that anyone had been there. And again there came the loud knocking at the door as police and people came to find out this time what it all meant. When, once more, they found nobody there save this same handful of people and children, they were amazed and couldn't believe their eyes.

But Father understood now. So did Christian and Ketty. They knew their prayers had been answered. They knew that God had sent His angels to protect them, and they had heard them singing!

Today that church still stands in Surabaya, a monument to God's protecting power, a testimony that the angels of the Lord still encamp around those who fear Him, to deliver them.

Small beginnings

Frank was happier than a dog with three tails. His uncle had given him a beautiful chemistry set for his birthday!

Inside the big box there were test tubes and beakers and glass rods and lots of little boxes of chemicals, even a bunsen burner! There was a book of instructions, too, telling how to make oxygen and hydrogen and all sorts of things.

'Oh, Dad!' cried Frank, as he lovingly picked up the various pieces of equipment and looked at them for the twentieth time. 'What a fantastic time I'm going to have!'

'Well, I hope you don't burn the house down,' said his father, 'or blow us all up!'

'I won't do that,' said Frank. 'But I'll tell you what I'm going to do. I'm going to invent something. I don't know what it is yet, but I am. I'm going to discover some new drug or chemical or . . . er — something, and make a lot of money. It's going to be like penicillin, and it's going to cure everybody of indigestion or rheumatism, and make a lot of sick people better. Then I'll get my name in the papers and everybody will be talking about me, and they'll be coming here to see me, and press photographers will come and take pictures of how and where the great discovery was made. . . . '

'Just a minute,' said his father, 'aren't you getting

a bit carried away? You haven't even taken a test tube out of the box yet! You haven't done a single experiment.'

'I know,' said Frank, 'but that brings me to something I wanted to say to you, Dad. I really should have a proper lab to work in, now I have all this equipment that Uncle has sent me. I'll need a place with a sink and hot and cold water. Oh, yes, and I'll need gas because of the bunsen burner. And, let me see. Yes, electricity too. And there should be plenty of cupboards to put all my things in.'

'Anything else, while you're at it?' asked his father.

'Oh, I'll think of more things as I go along,' said Frank, quite seriously. 'Do you think you could build a lab for me like this, Dad? A good place would be just beside the garage.'

'Ha!' laughed Father.

'What are you laughing at?'

'Just the way you carry on. It's so funny. Of course, I like you to dream of the great things you want to do later on, when you grow up; but you want to start the wrong way. You're all upside-down. Most big things start small, very small. And most people who've done big things have started in a very humble way.

'Edison, who invented so many things, began with the crudest tools. He certainly didn't have a nice lab with gas and electricity laid on, and a sink with chromium fittings.

'Franklin, another great scientist, learned the secret

of lightning with a kite made of a silk handkerchief and a key.

'Dr. Wollaston, when he became famous as a chemist, used to show his friends his first lab — a corner of a room where there was an old tea tray, some watch glasses, a small balance, and a blow pipe.

'So, Frank, if you want to become a well-known chemist, and make a name for yourself as one who has greatly helped his fellow men, go to it! But don't try to begin at the wrong end.'

'Can't I have a lab then?' asked Frank.

'Sure you can. You can have the little potting shed at the bottom of the garden. There's water there, and gas nearby. But you clean it out. You fix it up. It's better to start small and grow big, than to start big and fizzle out. And remember, it isn't the amount of equipment you have that matters, but ideas and persistence — just keeping at it.'

Frank was a little taken aback for a moment. 'I'd hoped you would build me a nice lab,' he said. 'But I'll take the old potting shed. And thanks, Dad. I'll fix it up OK, you'll see.'

'That's the spirit, son. I have some hope for you after all.'

A few minutes later Frank was running down the garden clutching his new chemistry set.

'Frank's Laboratories, here I come!' he shouted. Frank was on his way — from small beginnings to great results.

The hollow pie

Robert had the unfortunate habit of always taking the biggest and best of everything for himself.

His brothers, John and Peter, would call him all sorts of names for doing it, but it didn't seem to make any difference.

Mother was upset about it, too, especially as Robert, when invited out to parties, always disgraced the family by his greediness. What could be done? Mother put on her thinking cap and talked the matter over with her sister who lived in the next street.

A few days later the boys were delighted to receive an invitation to tea from their aunty. Remembering all the good things they'd enjoyed there in the past, they looked forward eagerly to the day of the party.

At last the day came and teatime arrived — for which Robert especially had been waiting.

The table was piled with good things, cakes, fruit, jellies, pies, chocolates and the rest.

Robert's eyes roamed around upon the wonderful spread of tasty dishes. 'Oh!' he thought, 'if only I had this little lot all to myself!'

Then he spied a beautiful pear on the fruit dish. It was one of the biggest he'd ever seen. There and then he decided to have it some time during the evening. He also looked around at the other things and made up his mind which of them he'd choose when the plates were passed around.

When all the visitors had been given their places around the table, tea began. Of course, they all started with bread and butter in the usual way. Robert, however, soon got tired of that. He wanted the big pie he could see on a plate at the other side of the table. Would he get it in time, or would Peter beat him to it?

The pies were passed around. John and Peter took small ones, and opened them. 'What wonderful centres they have!' thought Robert. 'Now, if only I can get that big one.'

Robert's turn came. The biggest pie was still there and, of course, he grabbed it greedily.

But disappointment awaited him. As he cut through the top, the whole pie collapsed. It was hollow!

Poor Robert! Tears filled his eyes, but as no one seemed to notice what had happened he ate the crust as bravely as he could and said nothing.

The cakes were passed round. Robert felt he was quite justified in taking the biggest this time, seeing there had been nothing in his pie.

But something was wrong with his cake. It looked all right outside, but the centre was bitter. What could be the matter? thought Robert. Aunty was generally such a good cook. And then, too, the others didn't seem to be having any trouble at all. It wasn't fair, he thought, but he didn't dare say anything for fear the others would laugh at him.

Now came the fruit. How thankful Robert was that the plate was passed down his side of the table first! He felt sure Peter was after that big pear. Anyhow, he would get it this time.

The plate reached Robert and he put his hand into the middle of the pile of fruit. Oranges and apples scattered in all directions over the tablecloth. But Robert got his pear.

His teeth were soon busy, but alas! something seemed to be the matter again. Taking his knife Robert cut the pear in two. To his utter disgust he found the centre was bad.

Still nobody seemed to notice Robert's plight, and no one passed him anything to make up for his misfortunes. Moreover, the others all seemed to be enjoying themselves to the full.

The chocolates came next, and by this time Robert was getting desperate. 'I shall have to make up for lost time by taking those two big beauties in the centre,' he said to himself, and then removed the two best-looking ones from the plate.

'Ugh!' said Robert, groaning inwardly. 'What a horrible taste!' Swallowing one with difficulty, he tried the other 'to take the taste away', only to find it worse.

On the way home Peter said to Robert, 'That tea was fantastic!'

'Not half!' said Robert (not willing to admit that, for him, it had been a disaster).

'But I thought you weren't enjoying yourself,' said

John. 'You looked quite uncomfortable. What was the matter?'

'Matter?' said Robert. 'Everything I took was bad, even though I took the best every time.'

'Maybe that was the cause of the trouble,' said John knowingly. 'I think if I were you I'd leave the biggest and best-looking things for somebody else next time.'

That night Robert stayed awake quite a long time. There were two reasons. One was a pain under his pyjama jacket, and the other was the advice John had given him. He put 'two and two together' and at last decided that the best and safest course for him would be to follow John's suggestion in the future.

How Donna lost her voice

This is a remarkable story. So remarkable, in fact, that you may be tempted to say, 'I don't believe that one!' But it really did happen, I can assure you.

Donna was just 7 at the time, and doing so well at school that Mother was very proud of her. But Donna had one fault — she always wanted her own way no matter what Mother said.

The problem came up again about the way Donna was to go to school. Mother wanted her to go one way, and Donna wanted to go another way. There was a lot of trouble at home.

'Darling,' said Mother one morning, 'I do wish you wouldn't take that short cut along the back streets. Sometimes the boys get very rough down there, and I wouldn't want anything to happen to you. Please keep to the main roads and then everything will be all right.'

'But, Mummy,' pleaded Donna, 'those back streets are quite all right. I've looked down them so many times and there's nobody about. It would save such a lot of time if I went to school that way.'

'It wouldn't even save you five minutes,' said Mother. 'Please go the other way. It's safer.'

'Well, I don't see why I shouldn't go that way,' said Donna, in a grumbly tone of voice.

'Maybe not,' said Mother, 'but, mind, *I* want you to keep to the main roads.'

Donna, pouting a little, went off to school. And because Mother's words were fresh in her memory, she went to school by the main roads — even though it was the long way round. But in the evening, when she was coming home, she began to think that after all, she was right, not her mother.

'I can't see why Mummy doesn't want me to go home the short way,' she said to herself. 'She just doesn't understand. If she were a little girl feeling as tired and hungry as I am, she'd take the short cut, too.'

So she argued with herself, finally feeling convinced that the short cut would be quite all right this time.

It was. There was hardly anybody in the back streets. Feeling greatly pleased with herself, Donna arrived home safely. But she didn't tell her mother which way she had come.

The next afternoon it was just the same, and the next, and the next. Sometimes Donna smiled to herself as she thought of how frightened Mother had been about the back streets. 'She doesn't know about them,' she thought. 'I just won't tell her.'

Then one afternoon it happened — the very thing Mother had been afraid of all the time.

As Donna walked home this time she noticed a group of boys outside a small shop. They were playing together quite happily. She didn't give them another thought. At least, not until she was quite close to them.

Then she saw they were playing a rather rough game called 'Dodgem', where the players throw a ball at some chosen person who is supposed to 'dodge' it. Unfortunately, not having a ball, these boys were throwing old tin cans, rotten cabbages and tomatoes, or anything they could lay their hands on.

Suddenly they saw Donna. She'd moved to the other side of the street for safety.

'Dodgem!' they shouted. 'Dodgem!' And they started to throw things at her just as hard as they could.

Donna began to run, but it was no use. The boys could run faster than she could. Soon they were chasing her down the street like a pack of wolves, each one hurling at her whatever he could lay his hands on from the street, all the time shouting, 'Dodgem! Dodgem!'

Poor little Donna couldn't 'dodgem', and soon her pretty dress was a terrible sight!

Of course, nobody meant to hurt her, but suddenly she gave a scream, clutched her throat, and fell over in the road.

The boys crowded round, wondering what could have happened. 'Her throat's bleeding,' said one of the biggest boys. 'Somebody must have thrown a stone.'

Somebody had. But nobody would say who. And, after all, what was the use of bothering about that now? The mischief had been done.

They tried to get Donna to tell them what was the matter. But she didn't reply. She couldn't. Then the boys became really frightened. One of them ran for a policeman. He picked up Donna in his strong arms and carried her home.

'Donna! What's the matter?' cried Mother as she opened the door. 'Donna! What happened?'

Still Donna couldn't speak.

Mother, talking to her all the time, took her indoors and bathed her throat. But Donna never said a word. She seemed to be trying to speak, but couldn't. Now Mother became very frightened and sent for the doctor. When he came he said the stone had been a sharp one and had struck Donna's 'voice box'. The injury was a bad one. Maybe she would never be able to talk again.

Some days later Mother took Donna to see a specially important doctor who knew all about 'voice boxes'. He said just what Donna's own doctor had said. They came away from the hospital feeling very, very sad.

Donna would never be able to speak any more!

When Mother was all alone, she cried and cried.

When Donna was all alone she thought how foolish she had been not to take Mother's advice. What a price to pay for her disobedience!

Months passed. The wound on Donna's throat healed, but she was still unable to say a word. By this time Mother had begun to believe she would never hear the voice of her little girl again.

Then one day there was another knock at the front door. Mother opened it to find a man selling books.

'No,' she said. 'Not today, thank you.'

'These are especially nice children's books,' he said. 'Maybe you have a little boy or a little girl. . . .'

Then Mother thought of Donna and invited the man inside.

As soon as the man saw Donna he brought out some of his books and began talking to her about them. He asked Donna what she thought of the pictures, but there was no reply. Surprised, he turned to Mother, but she merely put a finger to her lips and shook her head.

'Oh, I'm so sorry,' said the man. 'I didn't understand. Isn't there any hope?'

'None,' said Mother. 'None at all. We've tried every doctor, including a very important one down at the hospital.'

'There is another who might help,' said the man.

'Who is it?' asked Mother eagerly.

'The Great Physician,' said the man. 'Have you tried Jesus?'

'No,' said Mother, hanging her head a little. 'We haven't.'

'Would you mind if I were to ask Him?' said the man.

'No, of course not,' said Mother, 'if you wish.'

So the stranger got down on his knees beside Donna and prayed very simply that Jesus, in His great love, would give her back her voice.

Then he got up from his knees, said goodbye, and went on his way. Mother told him to bring Donna one of his books if he should come that way again.

A week later he returned.

As he was walking down the street towards Donna's house he saw a little girl running to meet him as fast as her legs would carry her.

'We're so glad you've come!' she cried, taking his hand in hers. 'We've been waiting for you.'

'For me!' he exclaimed. 'I say, I thought you were the little girl who couldn't speak.'

'Oh, yes, yes!' she cried. 'It happened the day after you left. Mother would have phoned you if she'd known your number. . . .'

There were tears in everyone's eyes as they talked over the wonderful thing that had happened. Then they got down on their knees and thanked the Lord who loves little children for what He had done for Donna.

Dream come true

Back in the 1890s young Covey was minding his father's sheep in the cold, desolate wilderness of Wyoming.

And what a wilderness! Not a house, nor a road, nor a tree, was to be seen. Nothing but the rock-strewn, shrub-covered land, with the snow-capped mountains in the distance. How the sheep found enough food to live in such a place is hard to understand.

Then came the blizzard.

A few moments later there was nothing to be seen but snow. Everything was covered — rocks, bushes, sheep and all.

Young Covey knew he hadn't a chance of getting back to the farmhouse. For one thing he couldn't see which way to go and for another all the familiar landmarks had vanished.

He knew that he was in great danger and recalled stories of people caught in blizzards who had been frozen to death and never heard of again.

Burrowing into the snow beside a rock he made a rough shelter for himself and some of the sheep which were nearest to him. Here he stayed all night. No bed. No fire. No food. No comfort of any kind.

It was January and the temperature dropped to 40 degrees below zero. The icy wind, blowing at fifty miles an hour, chilled him to the bone. How he stayed alive nobody knows. But he did.

All that night he longed for a warm fireside, something to eat, and woollen blankets. But there was no one to bring them to him. No one knew where he was.

As that long, long night wore on he thought what a blessing it would be if someone, some day would build a place of shelter in this lonely, desolate spot. Cold and hungry he dreamed about it until he almost thought it was true. But it wasn't. There was nothing to see but snow. Nothing to hear but the howling of the wind and the occasional bleating of the frightened sheep. Then he promised God that if his life was spared he would one day build a shelter here.

Should you ever visit the United States — Wyoming in particular — you might like to visit this spot.

All around there is still the same desolation. In the far distance the same mountains still lift their snow-capped peaks to the sky. But something is different.

In the very place where young Covey lay that night with his sheep, there stands one of the finest hostels to be found anywhere in the world.

Here are to be found the most comfortable beds, the cleanest bathrooms, and the finest food you could wish for. For breakfast you can have grapefruit, cornflakes and milk, and all kinds of other things that have been brought by lorry many hundreds of miles.

When I went there I felt that I had never enjoyed a meal so much. Everything was so delightful, and the service so efficient, that it was hard to believe that I was in the middle of a wilderness.

Naturally I wondered who had built such a lovely haven of rest in this remote, out-of-the-way place.

Who do you suppose it was?

Young Covey! Yes! He never forgot the dream he had that night of the blizzard, nor the promise he had made that, God helping him, he would one day build a shelter there.

He kept his promise, and kept it well.

Kidnapped

Have you ever wondered what it would be like to be kidnapped?

The thought is scary, isn't it?

Perhaps you've asked yourself just what you'd do if a stranger suddenly picked you up and hurried you away in his car.

Of course, all boys and girls know never to accept a lift from a stranger. But sometimes it isn't that easy. This is a true story of a boy who had such an experience.

Ricky was only 6 at the time this happened, and though he was very young, he liked to be useful and help other people.

When the minister of his church told about a hurricane that had blown away all the homes on a far-away island, Ricky decided to organize a sponsored walk to raise money. It was a good idea, and everyone said so.

First, Ricky went around the houses nearest to his home asking for sponsor money. Some people sponsored him for 5 pence a mile, others 10 pence, one lady even 50 pence.

Though only 6, Ricky walked six miles.

After that, it was a matter of collecting the sponsor money from the people in the houses around his home.

Everyone paid up — even the lady who had promised 50 pence per mile! He had almost finished. As he was walking towards home along the road, he noticed a car slow down. To his surprise it stopped beside him. A man he didn't know put his head out of the window and asked if Ricky wanted a ride.

'No, thank you,' said Ricky, remembering his mother's strict warning that he was never to accept a lift from a stranger.

'Oh, come on,' said the man.

'Thank you, but I'd rather walk,' said Ricky. 'I haven't got very far to go.'

The stranger opened the car door and got out. He caught hold of Ricky before he could run away.

'Get in there,' he ordered, picking Ricky up bodily and shoving him on to the front seat.

'But I don't want a ride!' shouted Ricky, struggling to get free. 'Let me out!'

It was no use. Already the door was slammed shut and the man had started the car. Soon they were moving rapidly along the road.

'What's your name?' asked the stranger.

'Ricky.'

'Who's your father?'

Ricky told him.

'Does he have lots of money?'

'I don't know,' said Ricky. At the mention of money he became more frightened, because he remembered the sponsorship money in his pocket which he'd collected that very afternoon. He hoped this man wouldn't find out about it.

Now the car was speeding past his home, and Ricky

saw all the places he knew so well being left behind.

'Oh, dear,' he thought. 'Where is he taking me?'

Then he remembered that Mother had said that if he was working for Jesus he need never be afraid because the angels would look after him. So he began to say a little prayer; but he was so frightened he hardly knew that he was speaking out loud.

'What was that you were saying?' asked the man.

'I was asking Jesus to save me,' said Ricky as the tears rolled down his cheeks.

For a moment the man hesitated, then as if making up his mind suddenly, he slammed on his brakes and the car screeched to a stop.

'Go on, go on, get out,' he snarled, pushing Ricky roughly on to the grass at the side of the road. Once again the door slammed and the car roared off into the distance.

As Ricky stood there wondering what to do next a woman from a nearby farm ran up to him and asked, 'What in the world are you doing all alone out here?'

Ricky told her all that had happened. Getting her own car she soon hurried him back to his mother.

Mother hugged him and said he was a very brave little boy. Ricky said he had been sure all the time that Jesus would help him.

I think He did, don't you?

Gary the glassbreaker

Crash!

'Oh, no, not again,' said Mum, who was sitting in the summer house.

'What was that?' asked Dad, rushing in from the garden.

'Another window, I'm afraid,' sighed Mum. 'The noise came from the kitchen.'

A cloud came over Dad's face. He and Mum went outside to see what had happened.

They didn't have far to look. One of the kitchen windows was completely shattered. There was glass all over the floor.

'Gary again, I suppose,' said Dad. 'Just wait till I catch him!'

Dad was right. It was Gary, but catching him was something else. He had disappeared.

'He'll come home for tea,' said Dad, as he picked up the phone to call the nearest glass shop.

Mum swept up the broken glass and returned to her chair in the summer house.

Suddenly there was another crash from far down the garden.

'Whatever is it this time?' called Dad from the dahlia bed.

'It must be the frame you grow your cucumbers in,' said Mum.

38

'That's the only glass in that part of the garden.'

They both ran down the garden and caught sight of Gary climbing over the back fence.

'Come back at once!' shouted Dad.

Gary came back very slowly. He knew that tone in Dad's voice.

Dad walked quickly to meet him, noting that one of the panes in his glass frame had been smashed.

'Did *you* do that?' Dad demanded.

'I didn't mean to,' stammered Gary. 'A stone sort of slipped out of my hand.'

'What about the kitchen window?'

'Well — er — another stone — er — slipped.'

'I think we had better go indoors and have a little chat about these slipping stones,' said Dad.

Gary began to cry.

'Crying won't help,' said Dad. 'I'm sick and tired of having you break all the glass around this house. At first it was the front window. Now it's my garden frame. These weren't accidents, but downright carelessness and vandalism. Who do you suppose is going to pay for all this damage?'

Gary was silent. 'Would you rather be made to stay indoors for a few weeks or pay for the damage?' Dad asked.

'Pay for it,' said Gary, 'but I haven't got any money.'

'Yes you have,' said Dad. 'You have some in the bank.'

'But that's my savings account. I'm keeping that for a new bike.'

'Too bad you didn't think of that before you threw the stones,' said Dad. 'The bike will have to wait. Instead you will take £2 a week out of your savings account until the whole bill is paid.'

'That'll take all my savings!' wailed Gary.

'That's just too bad,' said Dad. 'But you must learn that you can't go around breaking windows any time you feel like it. Glass costs money, and if you break it you must pay for it.'

'Oh, no!' groaned Gary.

'Oh, yes,' said Dad.

And that's the way it was.

Week by week Gary took £2 out of his savings account and gave it to Dad until the bill was paid and his account had hardly a penny left in it.

It was surprising how seldom stones slipped and windows got broken after that.

How Toby made peace

'Now look here, children,' said Daddy, bundling Paul and Julie out of the dining-room into the garden. 'I simply can't stand it any longer. You stay outside until you can learn to stop grumbling and be more polite.'

And with that, Daddy went back into the dining-room, sat down in his easy chair, put his feet up on the stool and went to sleep.

Paul and Julie knew they deserved their fate, and soon began to feel sorry that they had been such a nuisance to their father.

For a little while they didn't know what to do, and wandered up and down the garden path in silence.

'Ah, here's Toby coming!' cried Paul. 'Toby, Toby, Toby! Here, boy! Good old Toby. Where have you been?'

Toby wagged his tail, as if to assure them that he had been a very good dog all the time he'd been away.

'And you haven't been chasing any cats?' asked Julie.

Again Toby wagged his tail, as if to say that he wouldn't think of doing any such thing; although, if the truth must be told, there was nothing that so stirred Toby's spirit of adventure as the sight of a cat in full retreat.

'I've got an idea,' said Paul.

'Let's hear it,' said Julie.

'We ought to give Toby a bath. He hasn't had one for a long time and he's getting quite dirty again.'

'I think that would be fun,' said Julie. 'It's better than doing nothing. You get the bath out of the shed, and I'll slip into the kitchen quietly and get a towel and some soap.'

'Righto!' cried Paul. 'And won't that be nice, Toby? Toby have a bath. Good old Toby.'

Again Toby wagged his tail, though it wasn't quite so happy a wag as before. He wasn't over-fond of being bathed, and sometimes objected to it very strongly. He looked very suspiciously at the bath as Paul brought it out of the shed, and decided to take a short walk down the garden.

Julie returned, bringing a towel and a bowl of warm water. 'Where's Toby?' she asked.

'Run off,' said Paul. 'We'll have to catch him.'

'Toby, Toby!' cried Julie.

But Toby was a wise old dog and guessed why he was being called. He walked a little farther on. Paul and Julie followed him, and after an exciting chase caught him in a corner by the greenhouse.

'Bad Toby! Bad dog!' scolded Paul, as he dragged him by the collar up towards the shed. 'Toby mustn't run away any more. Toby's going to have a nice bath.'

Toby didn't appreciate the last remark at all, and by this time his tail had stopped wagging and a strange, determined look had come into his eye.

It was quite a job to get him into the bath. Paul lifted his front legs and Julie his back legs, and together they got him in. But it was quite another matter to *keep* him in. For a moment or two he stood quite still while Paul sponged his ears. Then he began to kick and jump and splash the water all over the place.

'Hold him, Paul,' cried Julie, 'or he'll jump out!'

'Can't you see I'm holding him as hard as I can?' said Paul. 'You get on washing him.'

Julie started, while Paul tried to keep Toby in the bath. She got as far as covering the whole of him with a good layer of soap, when something happened.

For a moment Toby became very still. He seemed to forget that he was being bathed. His eyes had caught sight of something down the garden. His back stiffened, his tail stood up, and with a loud 'Arf, Arf,' he shook his collar free, leapt out and dashed away at top speed.

'Stop him!' cried Julie helplessly, wiping the water from her dungarees.

'You'll never stop him!' said Paul. 'Look! It's Mrs. Tompkins' cat!'

'Oh, dear!' cried Julie. 'I do hope he doesn't hurt her.'

There was no fear of that, for this particular cat had often been chased by Toby and knew every possible hiding place in both the garden and the house.

'Oh, look!' cried Julie, as dog and cat raced hither and yon, across the flower beds, and in and out among the trees and bushes. 'Toby's getting in a dreadful mess!'

She was right. By this time Toby's soap-covered body had gathered up mud, leaves and bits of twig, until he looked as though he'd never had a bath in his life.

'I only hope Daddy doesn't look out of the window until we've got him cleaned up,' said Paul.

But there was no need for him to worry about Daddy. He was still sleeping soundly, quite unconscious of what was going on outside.

'Now you can catch him,' said Julie, as the cat did a sudden turn and came rushing up the garden towards them. 'Grab him as he goes by.'

But it was easier said than done. Paul made a grab, but his hand rested upon a greasy mixture of soap and mud, and away went Toby faster than ever.

'Look!' cried Julie. 'Look where the cat's going.'

They both looked. Growing tired, and seeking a place of safety, the cat had spied the half-open window of the dining-room.

With a mighty spring she leapt on to the window-sill, dropped down inside, and dived under an armchair that was drawn up near the fireplace.

Paul and Julie held their breath. Would Toby follow? Could he possibly jump that high?

'Toby!' they both shrieked, hoping to call him away.

It was no use. With a jump such as he had never made before, Toby got his paws up on the window-sill and scrambled over. He was in the dining-room.

Dirty, muddy, soapy Toby was in the dining-room!

All that happened next in the dining-room had better not be printed. Let's just say that Toby, forgetting the cat and spotting his master, jumped up in his usual friendly way onto the sleeping form in the armchair. With a start, Daddy found his hands clasping a strange, warm, wriggling, soapy mass upon his knees.

'What can we do?' said Paul. 'Daddy is going to be mad about this.'

'There's only one thing to do,' said Julie. 'We'd better go right in now and say we're sorry.'

'All right,' said Paul. 'I'll come with you.'

And away they went. They reached the dining-room, the French windows opened, and out came Toby, a little more quickly even than he went in. Daddy stood inside. He looked very stern. As for his clothes, they were a terrible sight.

'We're dreadfully sorry,' said Julie. 'We never dreamed he would do it, and we'll clean up all the mess and brush your trousers and everything. Please forgive us, Daddy.'

Daddy looked at the two children and at his clothes. Then the least bit of a smile began to curl about the corners of his mouth.

'Oh, you two terrible children!' he said. 'But I suppose I shall have to forgive you once again.'

And Paul and Julie put their arms around his neck and gave him a hug.

A tick at a time

Stephen was feeling very sorry for himself. Father had just asked him to take over the cutting of the front lawn as his share of the task of keeping his home and garden in good order. 'If you run the mower over it twice a week in the growing season, and keep it short,' Father had said, 'it won't be a serious burden at all.'

'No serious burden!' groaned Stephen as he half sat, half lay on the lawn with his head propped on the grass-catcher of the lawn-mower. 'No serious burden! It looks like one to me.'

Then he began to calculate what his new job would mean to him, for he was good at figures.

'This lawn,' he said to himself, 'is about twenty-two metres long and six metres wide. Given that the mower makes a cut about a third of a metre wide, that means I shall have to walk 450 metres every time I have to cut the lawn. Twice a week will make just about a kilometre. Phew!'

At this dreadful thought Stephen sank down a little lower on the grass. But his mind continued to work on the problem.

'One kilometre a week,' he said to himself, 'is fifty kilometres a year, allowing for some time when the grass isn't growing so quickly.' Fifty kilometres! This was too much for him.

Stephen continued to think over the problems of

this great distance until gradually his head slid down from the grass-catcher and he turned over on the grass, curled up and went fast asleep in the warm summer sunshine.

He was still fast asleep when Father came on the scene and took in the situation at a glance. His new plan didn't seem to be working very well. 'Hi, there!' he shouted. Stephen awoke with a start and jumped to his feet, a little ashamed of himself.

'What does this mean?' asked Father. 'No lawn done yet?'

'No,' said Stephen. 'I started to think about it, and found that if I cut this lawn twice a week for a year, I shall have to walk over fifty kilometres. That's too much. So, well, I suppose I just fell asleep at the thought of it.'

'Ha!' laughed Father. 'What an idea! You mustn't think like that! If anyone were to work out how much of an effort they'd have to put forth in a year on any regular job, they'd never have the courage to start at all. Just think of me. I have to walk nearly two kilometres to the bus every morning, and the same back at night. That's a lot of kilometres to total up for a year! If I were to think of that I'd give up now. I'd be too tired to go on. But by just taking a day at a time, well, it doesn't seem too bad. Maybe it helps to keep me fit.'

'Over a thousand kilometres a year!' whistled Stephen. 'I didn't think you walked that far.'

'Well, that's the way it is. And let's think of your

mother for a moment. She has five beds to make every day, which is thirty-five a week, or 1,820 a year. The very thought of making 1,820 beds is enough to make me feel completely worn out.

'Besides that, Mum has to wash up at least 150 items a day, including dishes, glasses, knives, forks and spoons. That makes over 1,050 a week, or 54,600 a year. Imagine that, if you want to feel tired! Add to that 250 pieces of laundry to wash each week, or 13,000 a year. Yes, and 70 kilogrammes of food to prepare each week, or 3,640 kilogrammes a year. It's terrifying if you look at it all at once.'

'I should say it is,' said Stephen. 'Think of washing 50,000 dishes! I'd die! I'm sure I would!'

'It's obvious, Stephen, that we mustn't look at life that way. It would be too hard on all of us. We must live a day at a time. That's how God intended us to live. "As thy days, so shall thy strength be," He says in Deuteronomy 33:25. Not "as thy week", or "as thy month" but "as thy days".

'I think', continued Father, 'that we could all learn a good lesson from the pendulum of the old grandfather clock. The story is told that "once upon a time" a pendulum started to think. Then it began to add up the number of times it swung to and fro. One swing a second, sixty swings a minute, 3,600 swings an hour, 86,400 a day, 31,536,000 a year. When the pendulum got that far, it promptly stopped swinging, and people wondered why the old clock had stopped. Even a pendulum must do one swing at a time and forget the rest. So must we. Moment by moment, hour by hour, day by day, we must do the best we can. Then life won't seem so hard. And we shall have strength for every task we have to do.'

'Well,' said Stephen, 'I suppose I shall have to forget those 50 kilometres of walking, and cut the lawn once, today.'

'A splendid idea,' said Father. 'The only way to look at it.'

Just a few moments later a comfortable purring noise could be heard in the garden as Stephen and the lawn-mower began to move at last, cutting beautiful swathes across the lawn.

Not afraid any more

Six-year-old Karen had just been given a brand new bicycle for her birthday, and she was happy!

It didn't take her long to get used to it, and soon she was riding it all over the place.

'I wish you'd be a bit more careful,' said Mother one day. 'I think you're taking too many risks.'

'I'll be all right,' said Karen. 'I'll never fall off.'

But that's exactly what she did. She took one risk too many and over she went with a bang.

Mother was in the house at the time, but she recognized the wild screams coming from outside. She ran out and there was Karen lying on the footpath, blood running down her face, and her precious bicycle lying on top of her.

'I think she rode her bike too near the edge,' said a neighbour who was trying to lift the bicycle off Karen. 'I hope she's not badly hurt.'

'Thanks for helping,' said Mother, as she picked up her little girl and ran indoors with her, the neighbour following.

'She has a bad cut on her forehead,' said Mother. 'I hope she didn't get a fracture too.'

'Better take her to the hospital right away,' said the neighbour. 'I'll drive you in my car.'

The mention of the word 'hospital' made Karen scream again. The very thought terrified her. But off

they all went and half an hour later she was lying on a bed in the emergency room.

Mother tried to comfort her. 'It won't take long,' she said. 'The doctor will soon tell us what's the matter. Then he'll give you something that will make you better again.'

The doctor didn't come for what seemed a very long time. He was so busy looking after other patients he just couldn't come right away.

The waiting was hard to take, especially when the doctor started to help the little boy in the next bed.

That was when Mother whispered to Karen: 'Why don't we ask Jesus to help you not to be afraid?'

'All right,' said Karen. 'Let's do that.'

So they both prayed together. When it came to Karen's turn she said: 'Please, Jesus, don't let me be afraid any more. Take all my fears away.'

It was a very simple prayer, but somehow it worked. She lay back on her pillow, relaxed and was peaceful.

When at last the doctor came she looked up at him and smiled. He smiled back at her and made a joke when he was giving her a 'shot'.

After he had examined her head he said she was lucky not to have a fracture, but he would have to put in a few stitches to hold the skin in place.

After he had gone Karen said: 'It's a strange thing, Mummy, but I never felt a thing. And I never worried once. I think Jesus answered my prayer.'

'I think so, too,' said Mother. 'The Bible says

"Blessed are all they that put their trust in him." (Psalm 2:12.) That includes us, you and me. It means we can be happy and at peace wherever we are and whatever happens to us.

'And that reminds me of another lovely verse: "In God have I put my trust: I will not be afraid what man can do unto me" — not even the doctors! (Psalm 56:11.)

'So if we love and trust Him, He will bring us peace whenever our hearts are troubled, just as He made the storm calm on Galilee in the long ago.'

Why the light went out

One stormy night in November 1950 a lighthouse on the coast of Denmark suddenly went out.

Four ships happened to be steering past the light at that moment. When it went out they lost their way. All four ran aground. Three of them were destroyed.

This meant a big loss to the owners. So an inquiry was made as to why the light went out.

Engineers were sent to the lighthouse. They took the lamp apart. And what do you suppose they found? You'd never guess.

Somehow or another an earwig had crawled into the burner and stopped the fuel supply. That one little insect had wrecked four ships!

But it isn't just earwigs that can do a lot of damage like this. King Solomon once wrote about 'little foxes' that 'spoil the vines'. He wasn't worried about the big ones. They could be seen and caught easily. It was the little ones that worried him.

It's that way with little faults. They may not be much to look at, but once you let them into your life and make a habit of them, they will spoil everything. You'll never be the same again.

I remember a fine-looking boy who, after being at school a little while, picked up some swear words from

the other boys. Some people thought it was funny to hear him use them. But it wasn't funny. Soon he was swearing all the time. He lost all the sweet innocence of his childhood. The light went out of his life.

I remember a lovely little girl, so dear and kind and good. But after she had been at school for a while she noticed that other little girls painted their faces — even though it was against the school rules! At first people smiled and thought it was funny. But it wasn't a joke, really. After a while she became vain and proud and foolish. She too lost her innocence. It was such a little thing, but the light of her life went out.

I remember a boy who wanted to be a missionary when he grew up. But another boy gave him some tobacco to smoke. It wasn't very much. Just one cigarette. But he got a taste for smoking and he couldn't give it up. Like millions of others he became a slave to it. He didn't want to be a missionary any more. The light of his life had gone out.

How careful we should be to keep the earwigs out of our lives. Not only can they put us in darkness; they can wreck those other ships whose captains are following the light of our example.